PUZZLE TIME
KAKURO BOOK
BOOK 3

100 PUZZLES
BEGINNER TO ADVANCED

KAKURO

If you thought Sudoku was fun – wait until you've tried the great Kakuro!

Kakuro is similar to Sudoku, but it uses a different shaped and sized grid. Kakuro could also be mistaken for a Crossword at first glance, due to its empty and filled squares – however this puzzle is easily as good as, and some might say better than those two family favourites! Kakuro is already more popular than Sudoku in Japan and since it hit British shores in the pages of a daily newspaper, it has proved to be extremely popular, even threatening to become Britain's favourite puzzle!

Devilishly difficult at times and yet stunning in its simplicity, this particular mind-boggler will leave you glowing with satisfaction when you complete it!

Kakuro puzzles are derived from an American puzzle called Cross Sums. The Japanese puzzle publisher, Mckee Kaji, created the name "Kakuro".

How to Play

The filled squares have a diagonal line from top left to bottom right. There are numbers within these squares that act as clues to help you complete the puzzle. The numbers above the diagonal line are clues going across to the right and the numbers beneath the diagonal line are clues going down.

You need to fill the blank squares following the clues (either to the right or down) with single numbers which when added together match the clues.

Only a single digit can be used per square, and the same digit cannot occur in the same row of squares adding up to the same clue. For example, if the clue is 8, and there are 2 empty squares, you cannot use 4 + 4, you would instead have to use 3 + 5 or 5 + 3 (depending on how the square fits with any clues running downwards or across using the same box). You could also use 6 + 2, 1 + 7 – you get the idea. That may sound simple – but Kakuro gets difficult and extremely addictive.

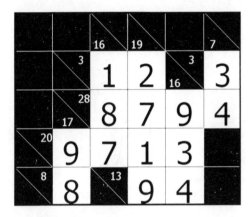

Though it is possible, try not to guess numbers because that can really throw you off-course, remember, every puzzle is solvable.

Well, that's about all you need to get you going, enjoy tackling the new phenomenon that is,

KAKURO!

PUZZLE 1

EASY

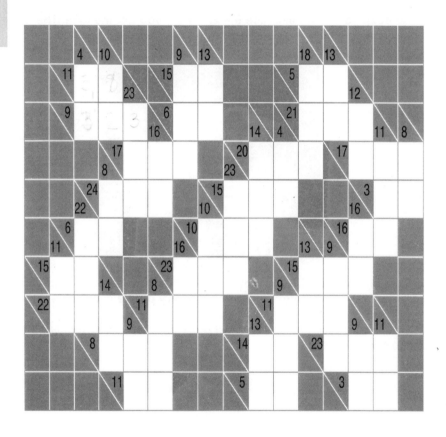

PUZZLE 2

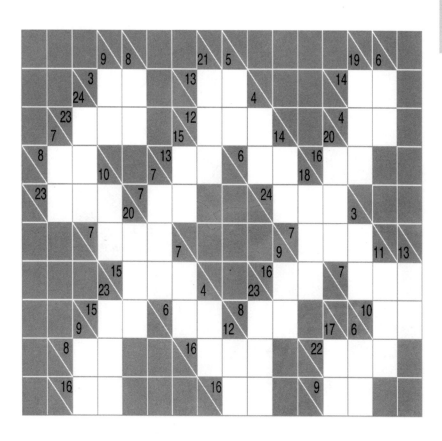

PUZZLE 3

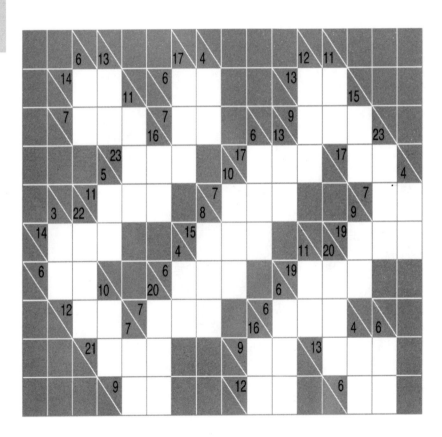

PUZZLE 4

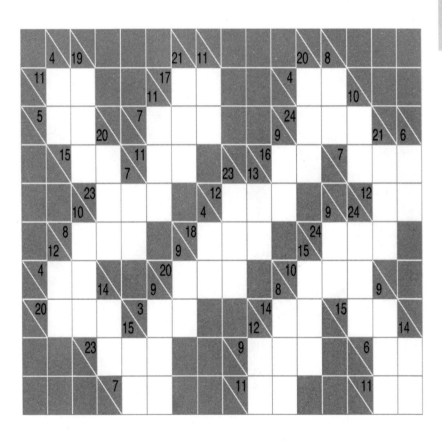

PUZZLE 5

EASY

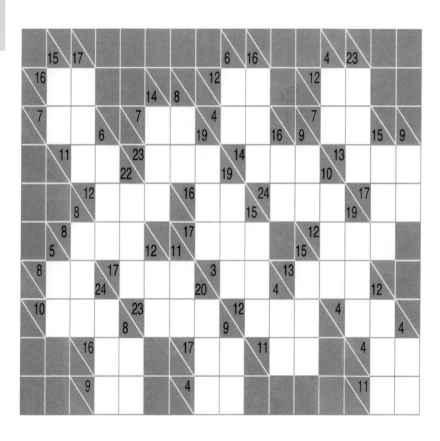

PUZZLE 6

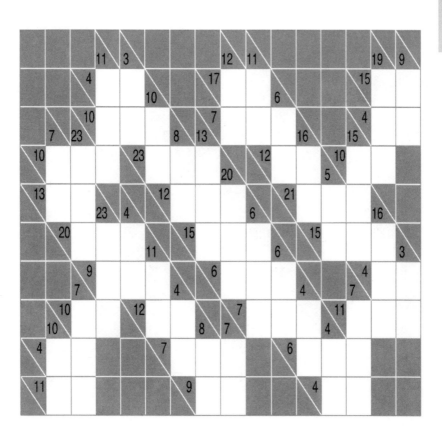

PUZZLE 7

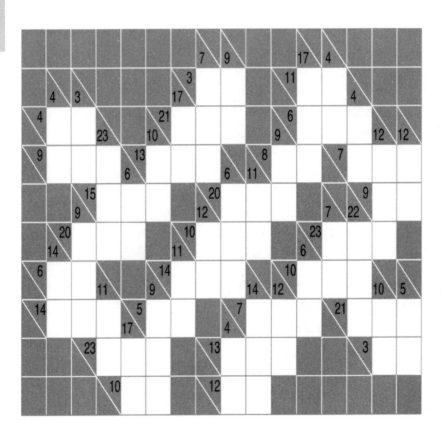

PUZZLE 8

EASY

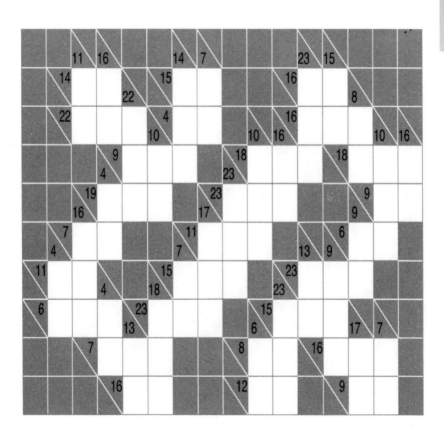

PUZZLE 9

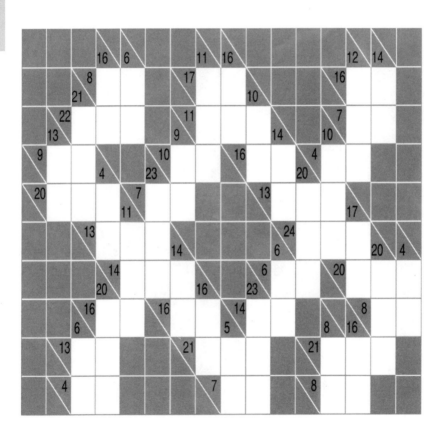

PUZZLE 10

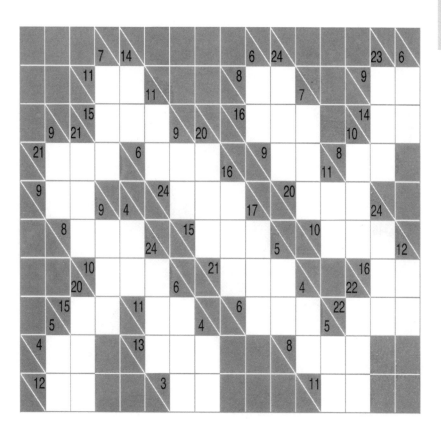

PUZZLE 11

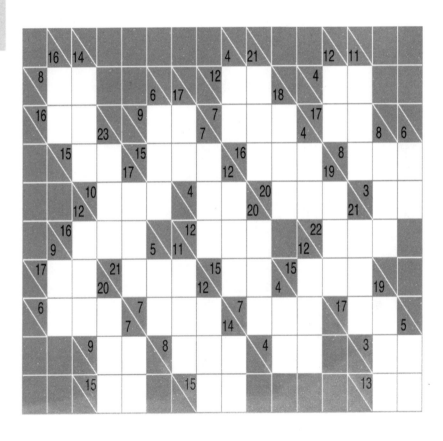

PUZZLE 12

PUZZLE 13

EASY

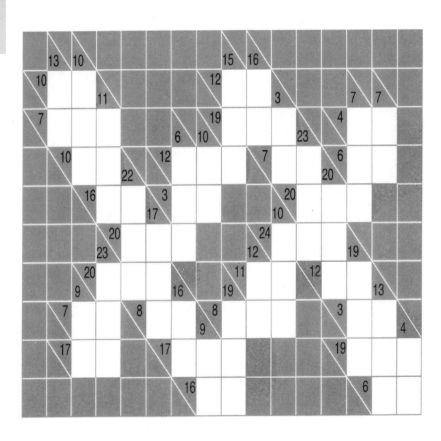

PUZZLE 14

EASY

PUZZLE 15

EASY

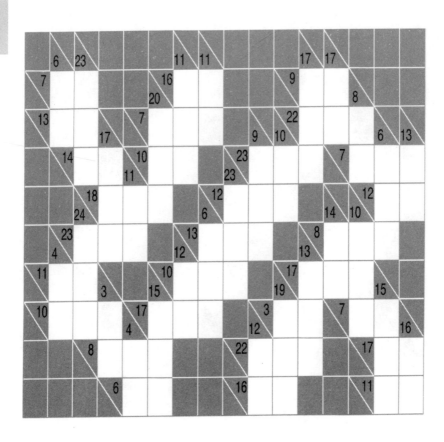

PUZZLE 16

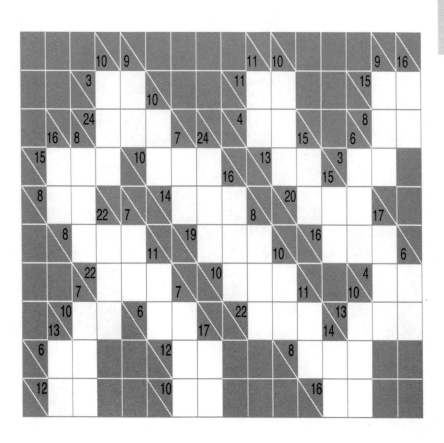

PUZZLE 17

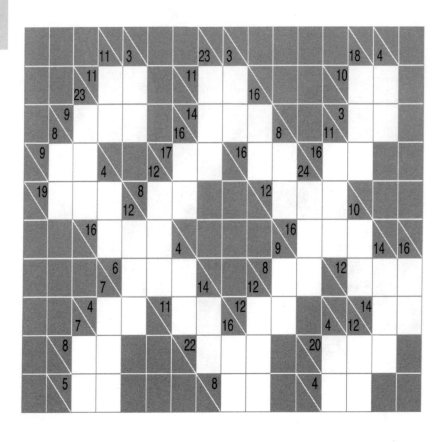

PUZZLE 18

PUZZLE 19

EASY

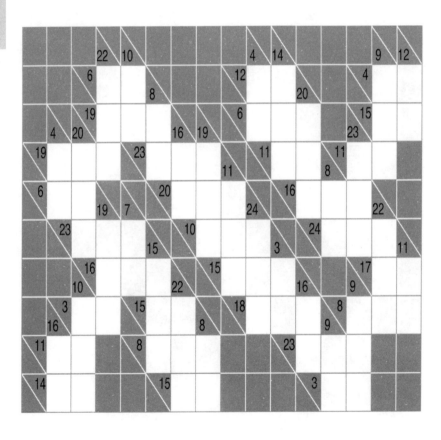

PUZZLE 20

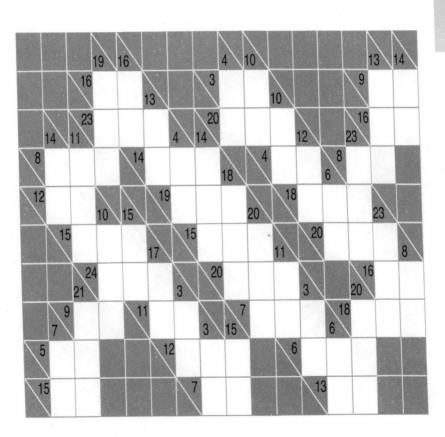

PUZZLE 21

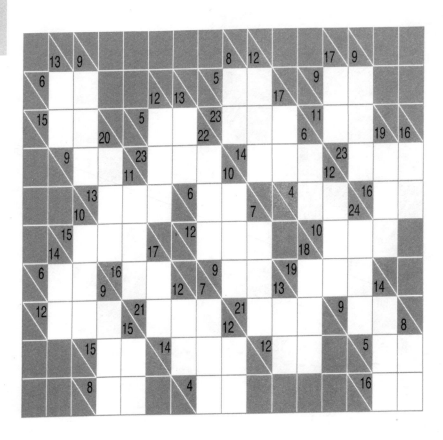

PUZZLE 22

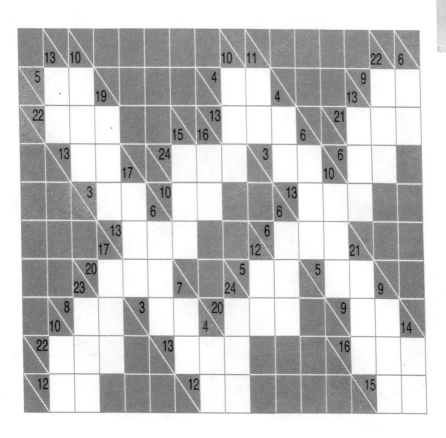

PUZZLE 23

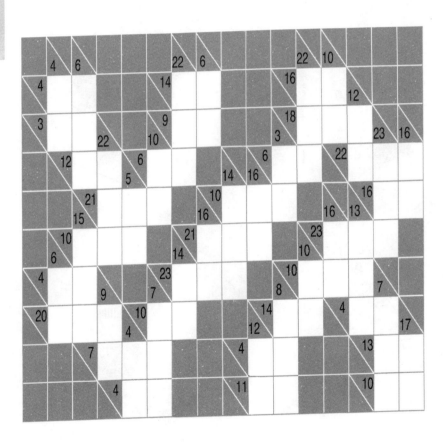

PUZZLE 24

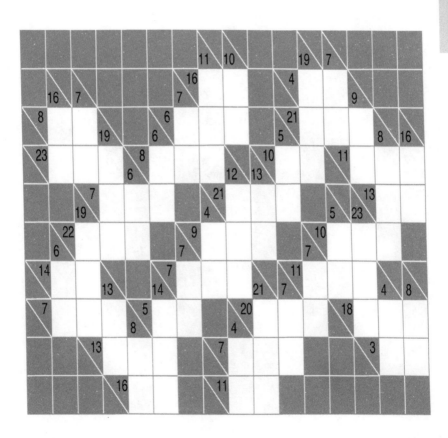

PUZZLE 25

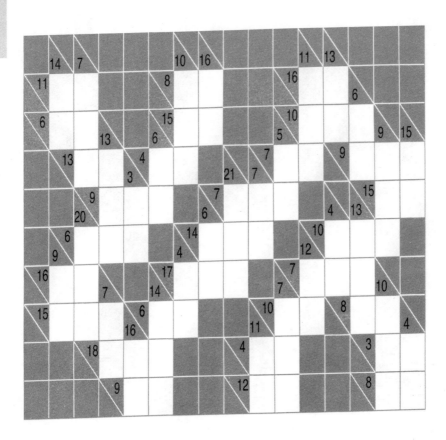

PUZZLE 26

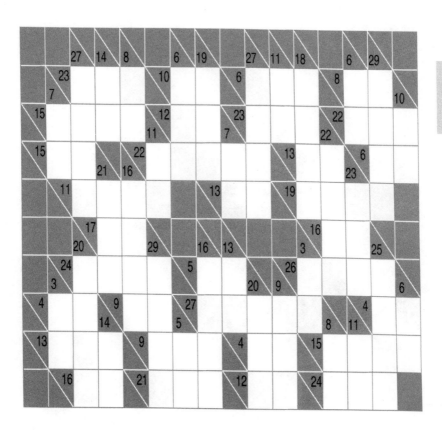

MILD

PUZZLE 27

MILD

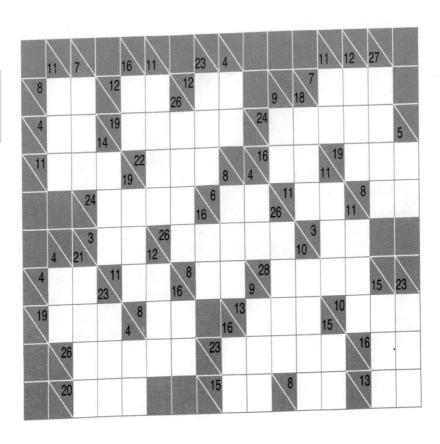

PUZZLE 28

MILD

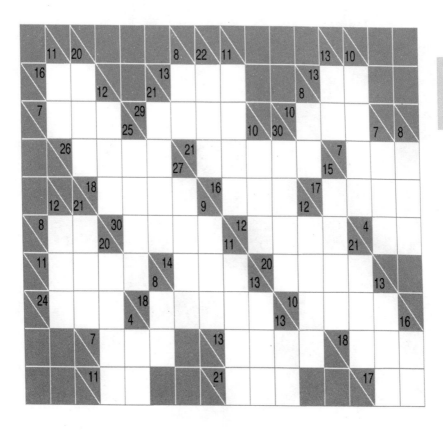

PUZZLE 29

MILD

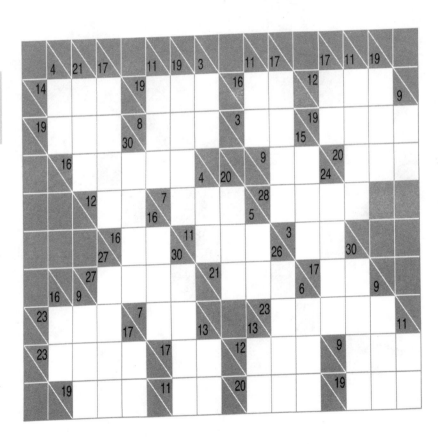

PUZZLE 30

MILD

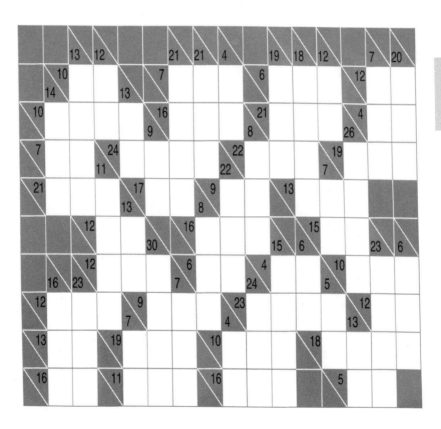

PUZZLE 31

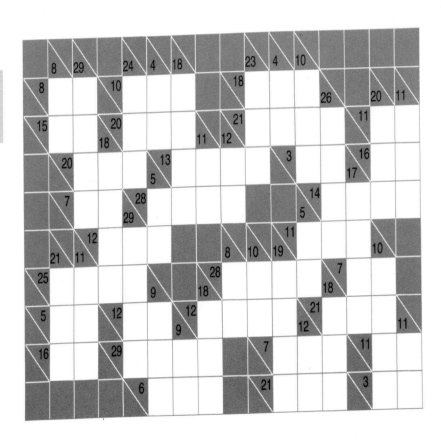

PUZZLE 32

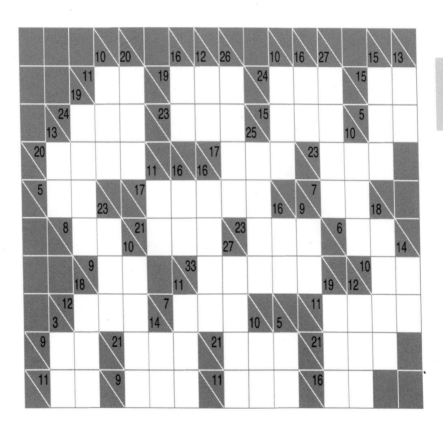

MILD

PUZZLE 33

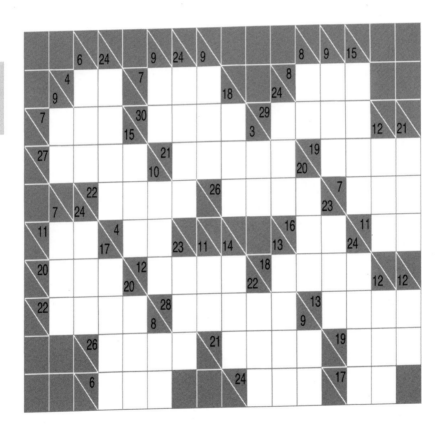

PUZZLE 34

MILD

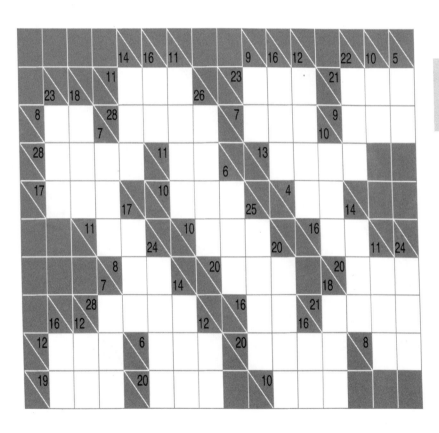

PUZZLE 35

MILD

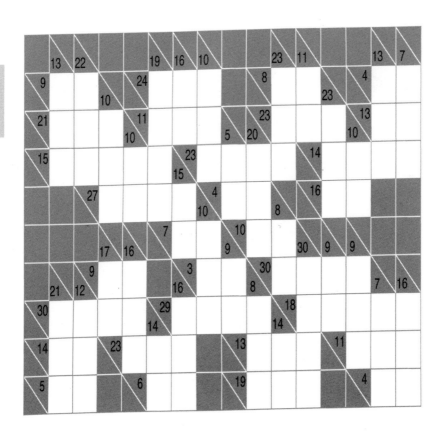

PUZZLE 36

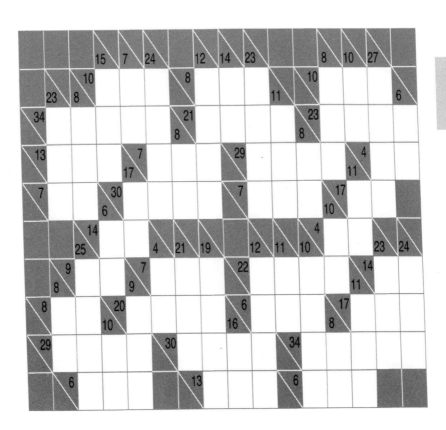

PUZZLE 37

MILD

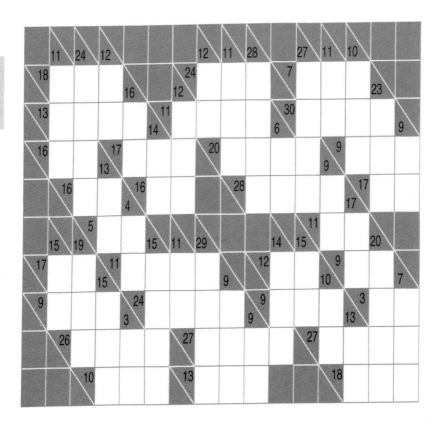

PUZZLE 38

MILD

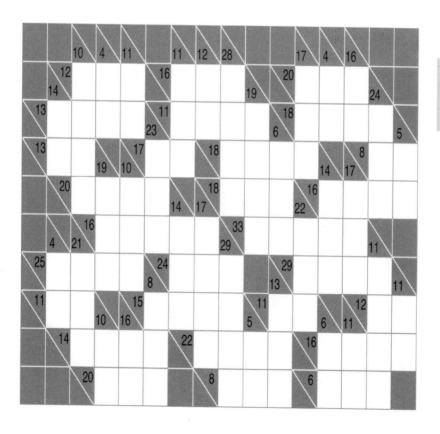

PUZZLE 39

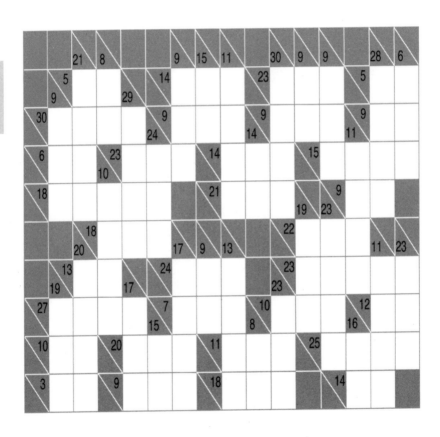

PUZZLE 40

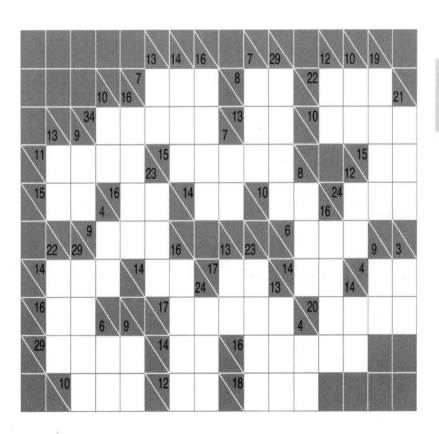

MILD

PUZZLE 41

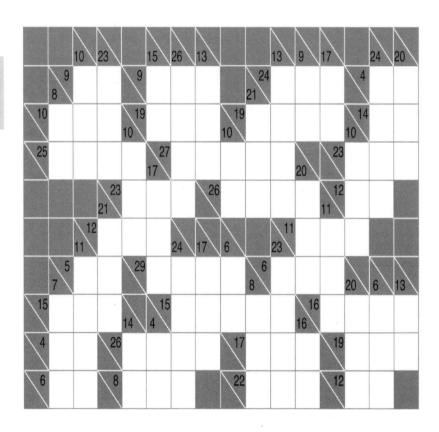

PUZZLE 42

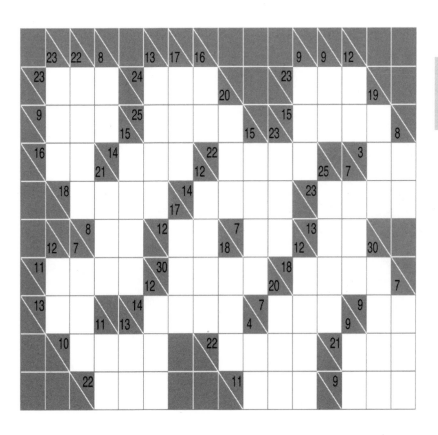

PUZZLE 43

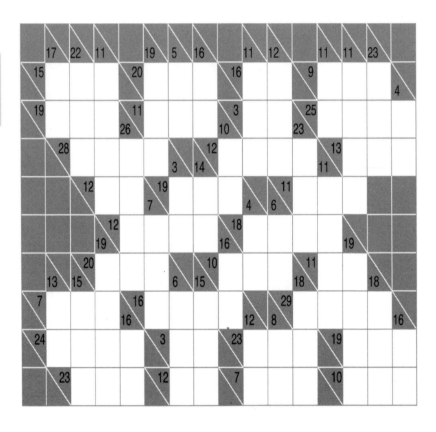

PUZZLE 44

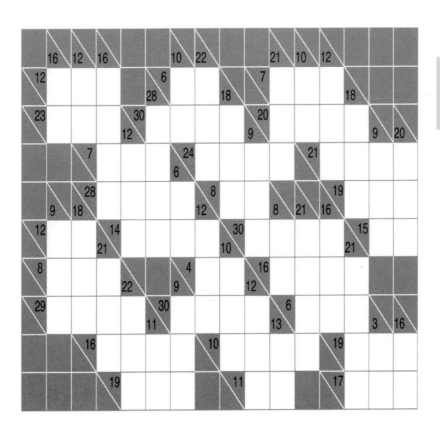

PUZZLE 45

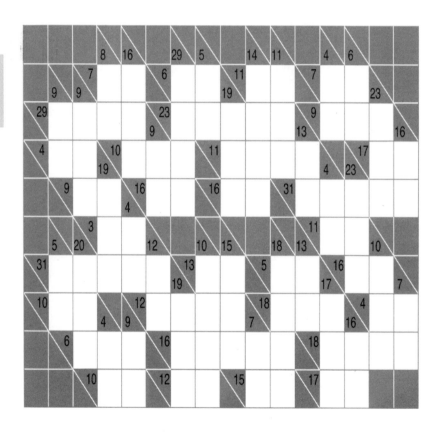

PUZZLE 46

MILD

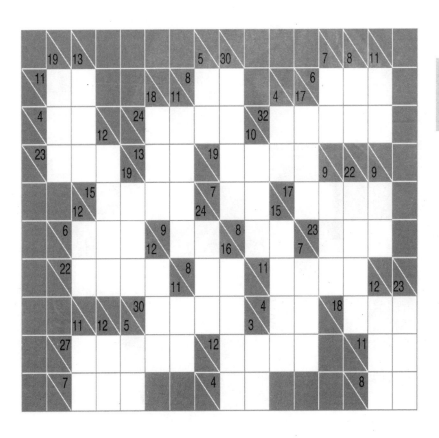

PUZZLE 47

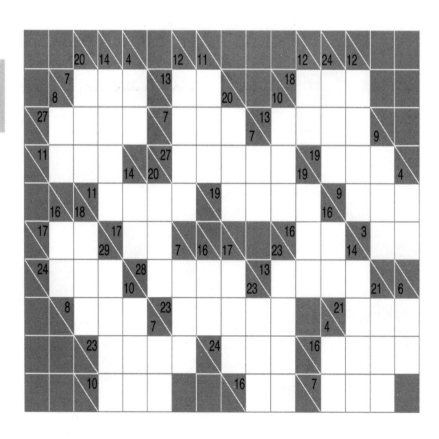

PUZZLE 48

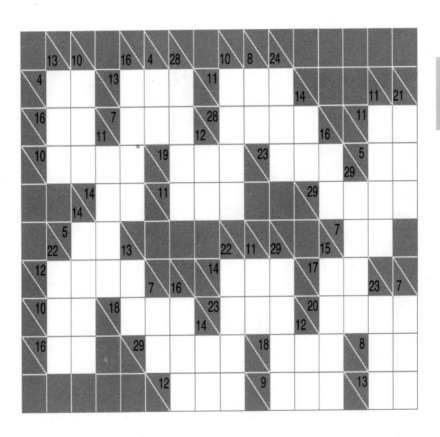

PUZZLE 49

MILD

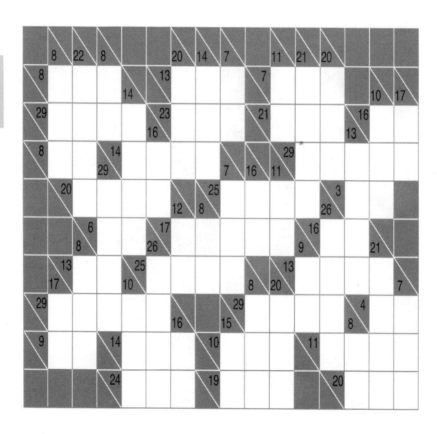

PUZZLE 50

MILD

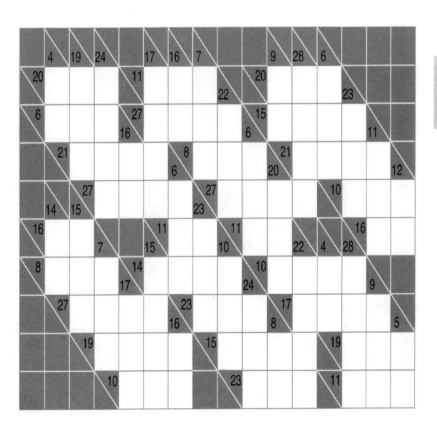

PUZZLE 51

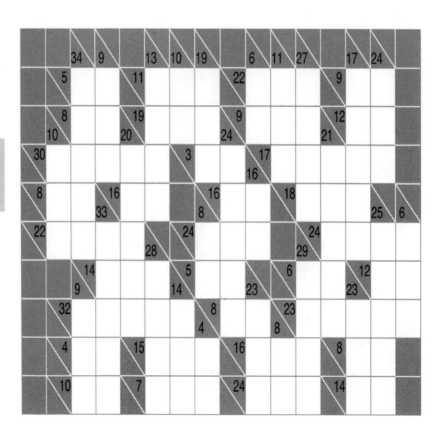

PUZZLE 52

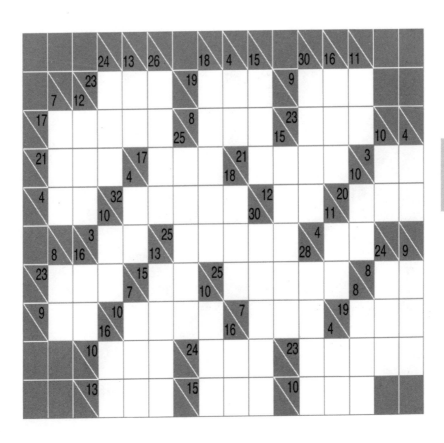

DIFFICULT

PUZZLE 53

DIFFICULT

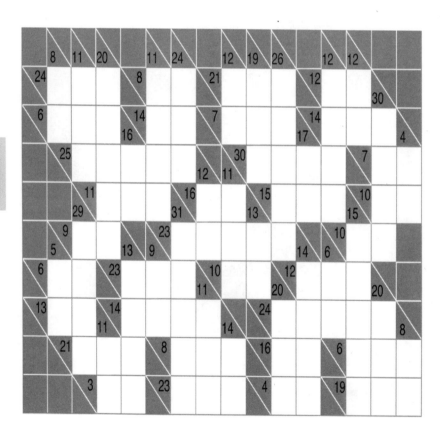

PUZZLE 54

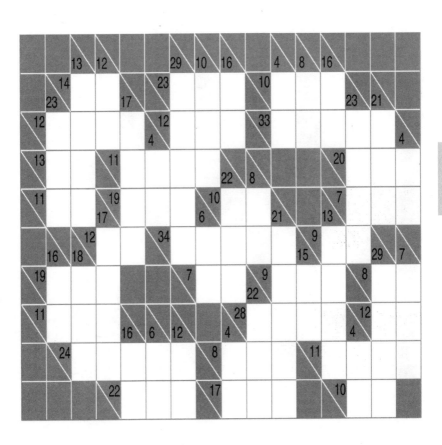

DIFFICULT

PUZZLE 55

DIFFICULT

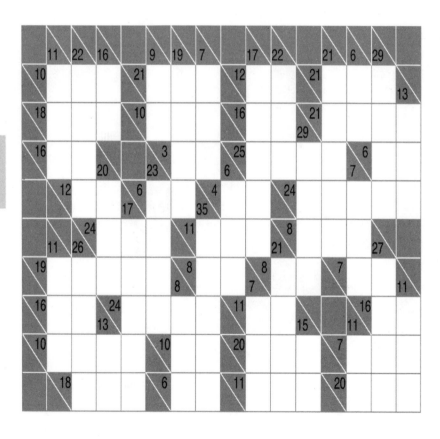

PUZZLE 56

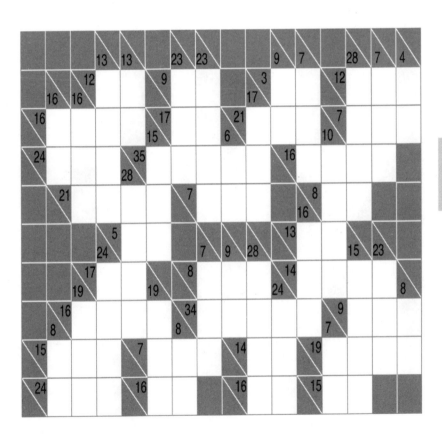

PUZZLE 57

DIFFICULT

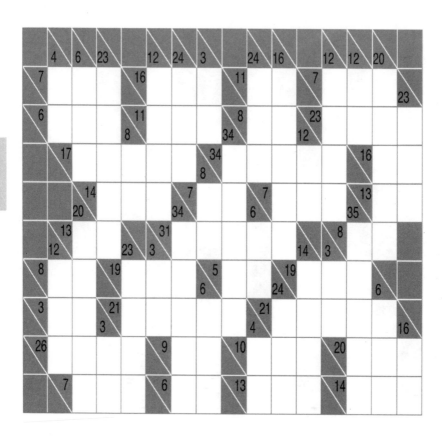

PUZZLE 58

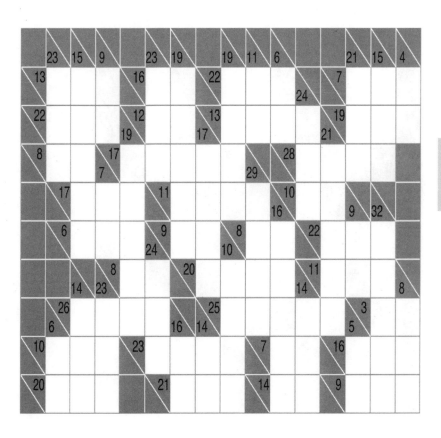

PUZZLE 59

DIFFICULT

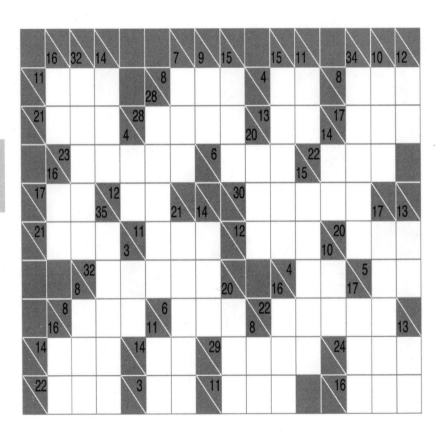

PUZZLE 60

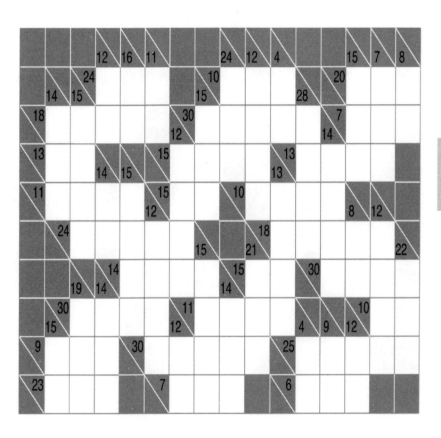

DIFFICULT

PUZZLE 61

DIFFICULT

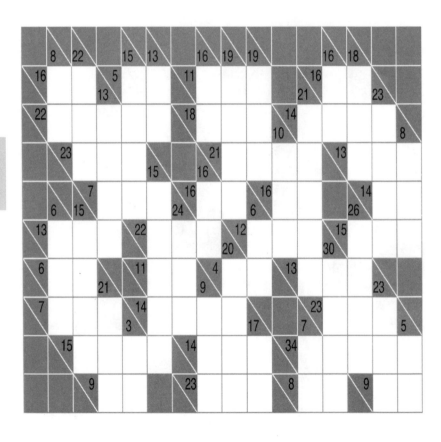

PUZZLE 62

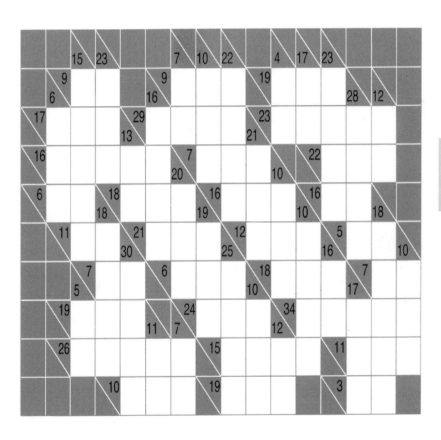

PUZZLE 63

DIFFICULT

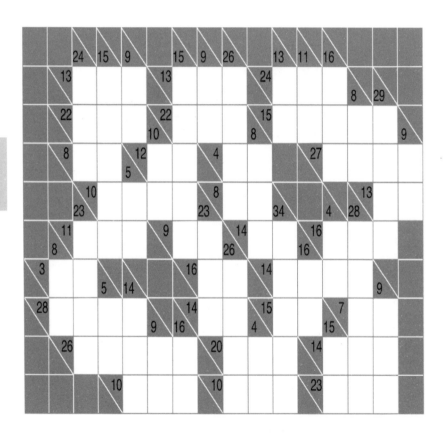

PUZZLE 64

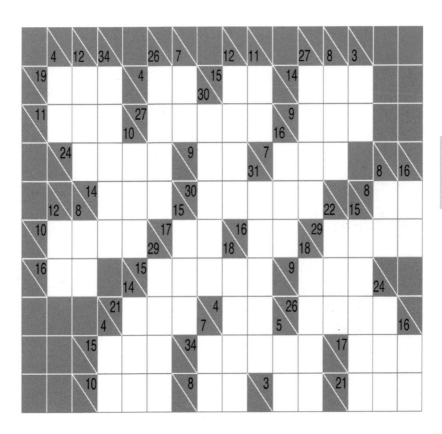

DIFFICULT

PUZZLE 65

DIFFICULT

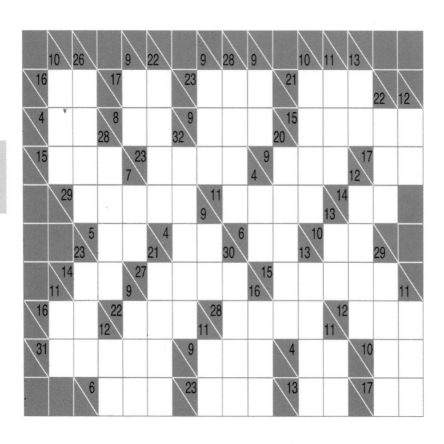

PUZZLE 66

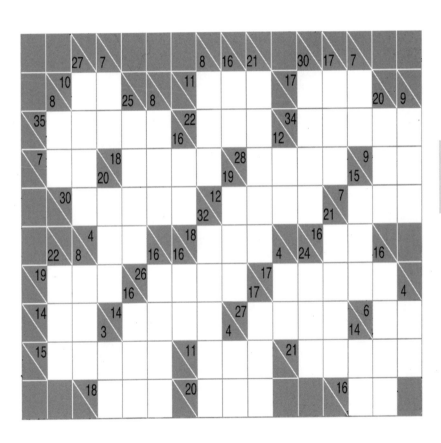

DIFFICULT

PUZZLE 67

DIFFICULT

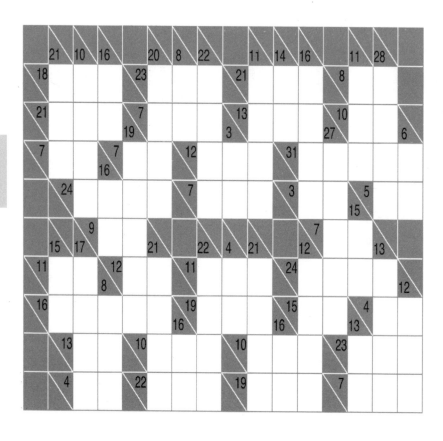

PUZZLE 68

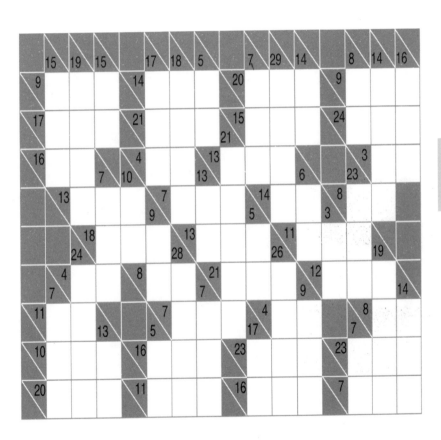

PUZZLE 69

DIFFICULT

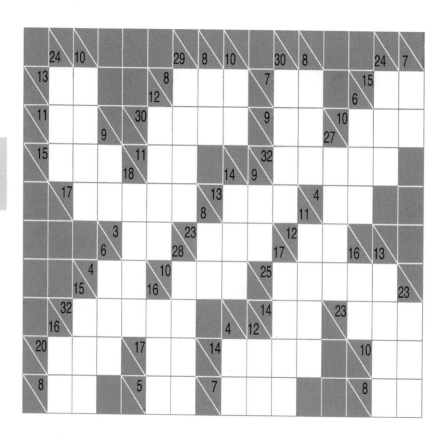

PUZZLE 70

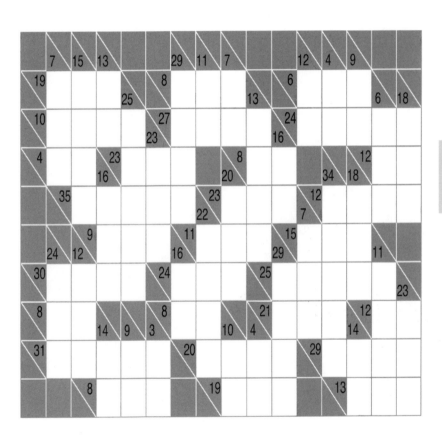

PUZZLE 71

DIFFICULT

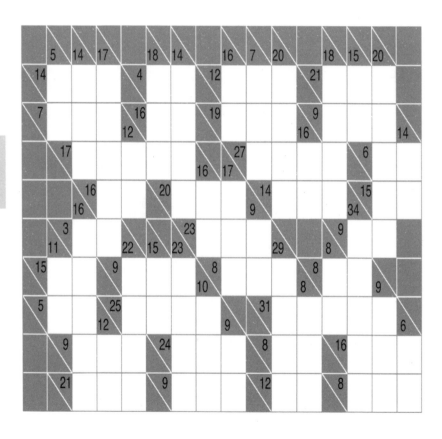

PUZZLE 72

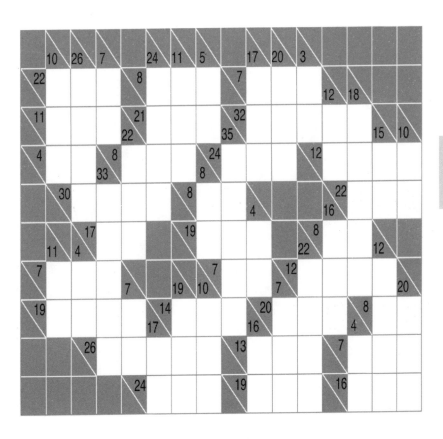

DIFFICULT

PUZZLE 73

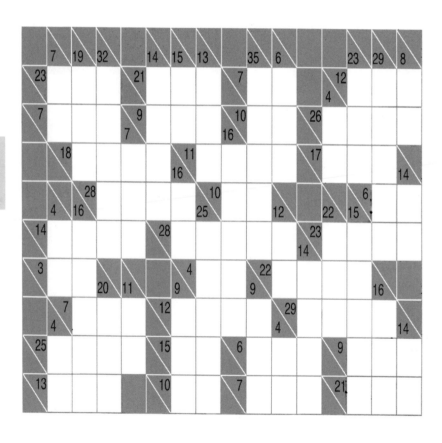

PUZZLE 74

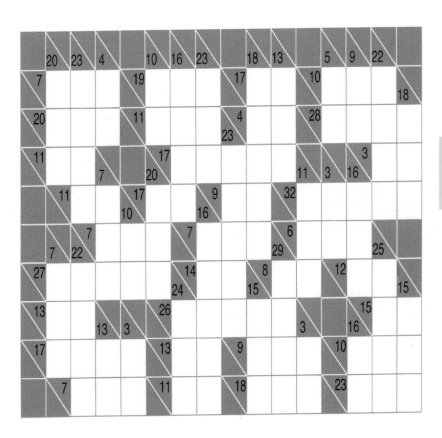

PUZZLE 75

DIFFICULT

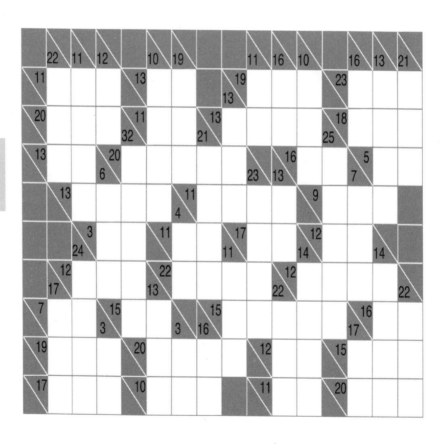

PUZZLE 76

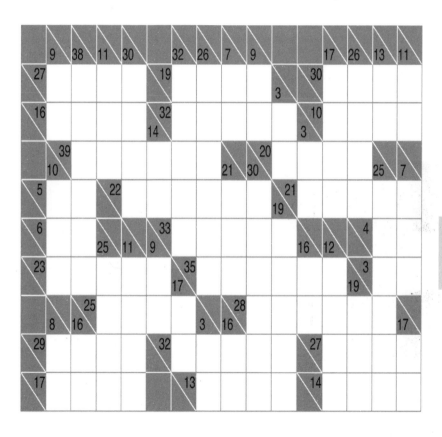

FIENDISH

PUZZLE 77

FIENDISH

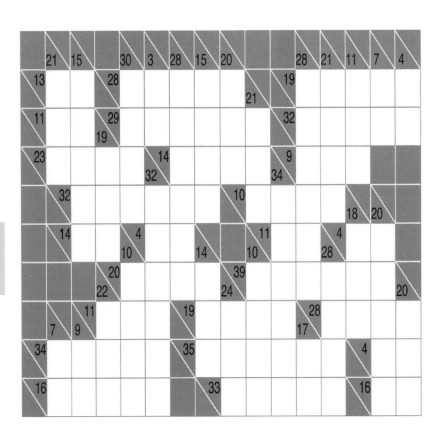

PUZZLE 78

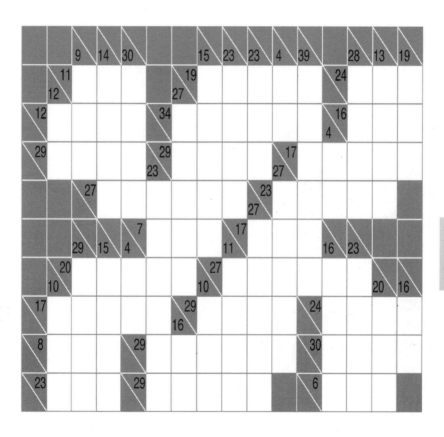

FIENDISH

PUZZLE 79

FIENDISH

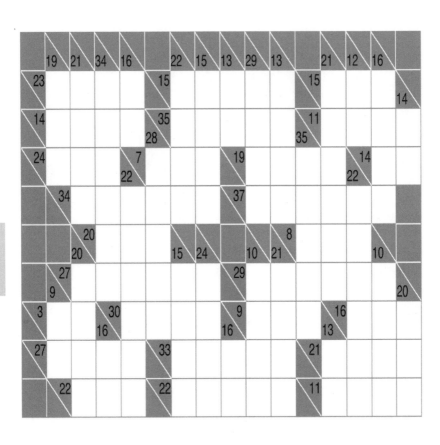

PUZZLE 80

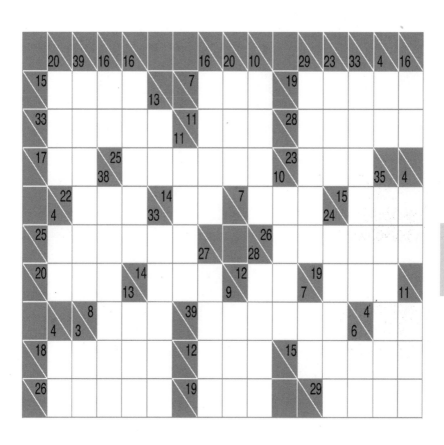

FIENDISH

PUZZLE 81

FIENDISH

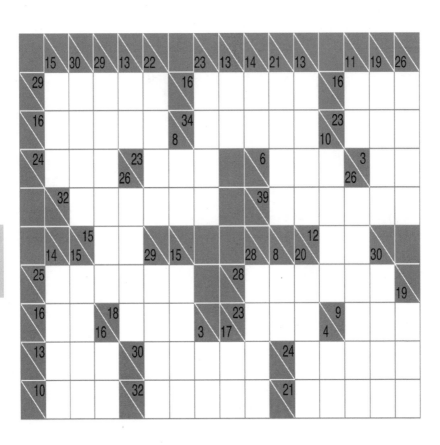

PUZZLE 82

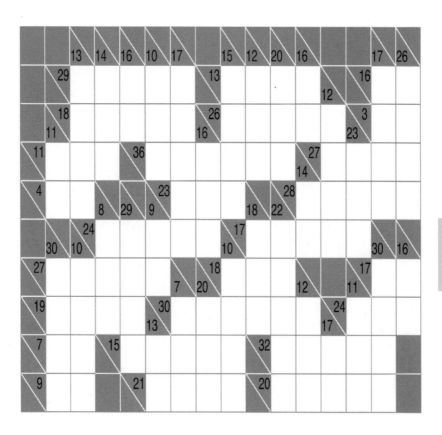

FIENDISH

PUZZLE 83

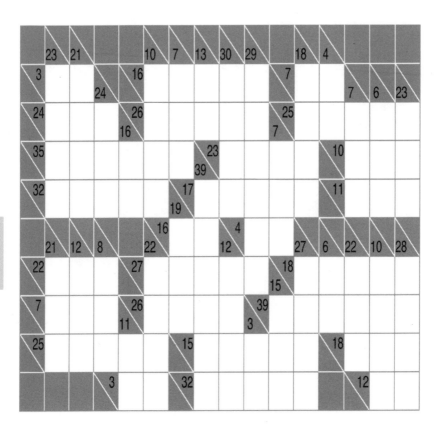

PUZZLE 84

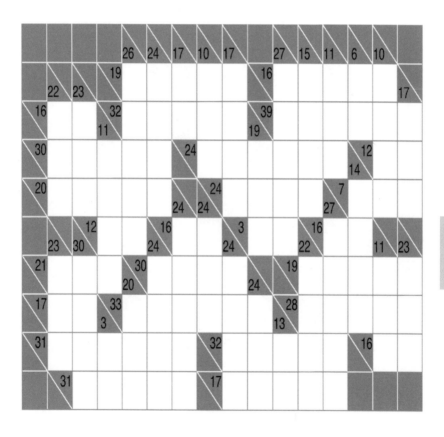

PUZZLE 85

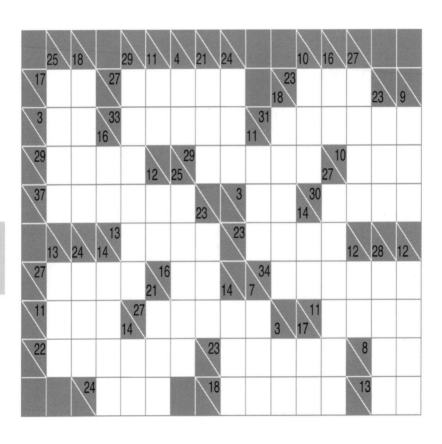

PUZZLE 86

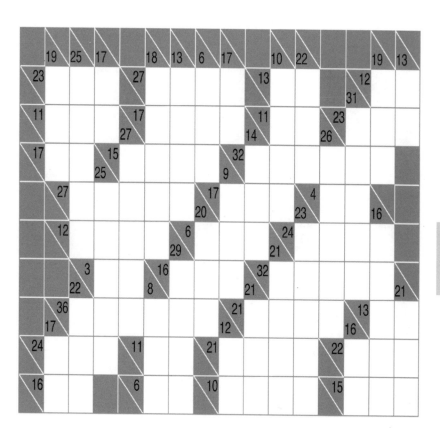

FIENDISH

PUZZLE 87

FIENDISH

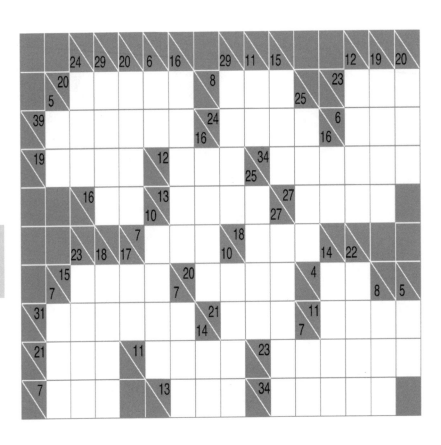

PUZZLE 88

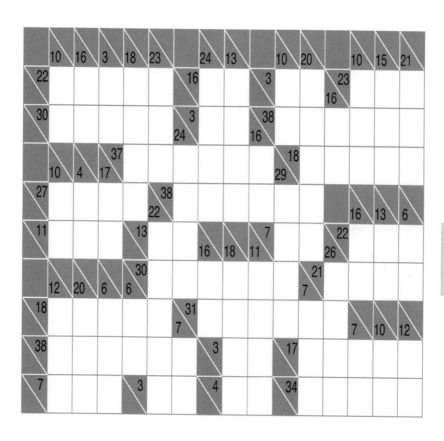

FIENDISH

PUZZLE 89

FIENDISH

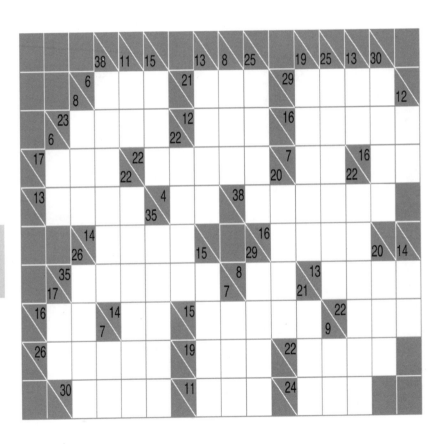

PUZZLE 90

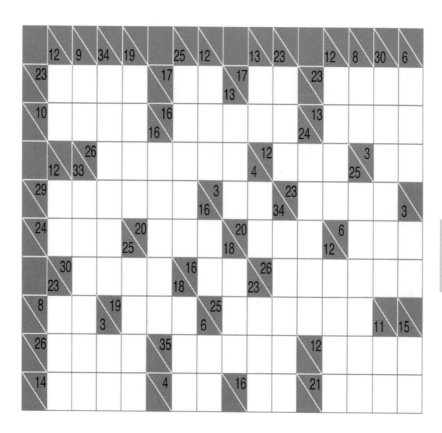

FIENDISH

PUZZLE 91

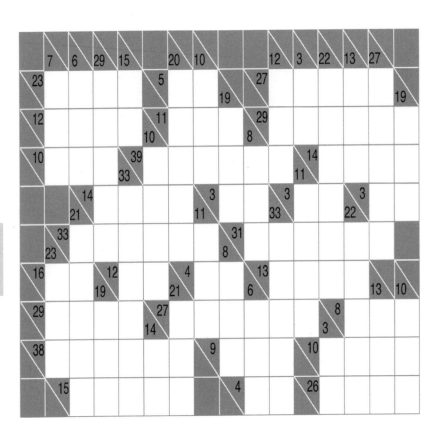

PUZZLE 92

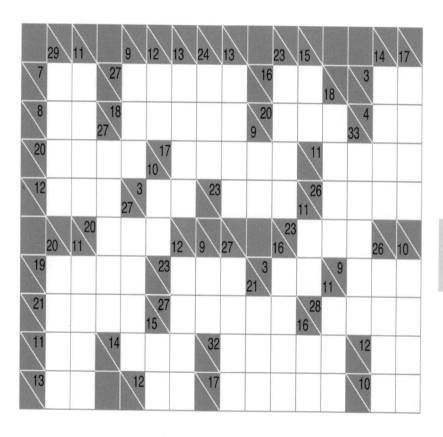

FIENDISH

PUZZLE 93

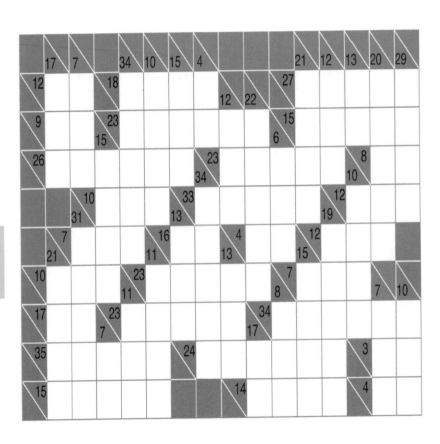

PUZZLE 94

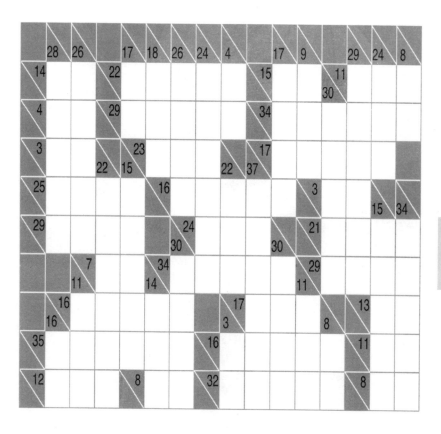

FIENDISH

PUZZLE 95

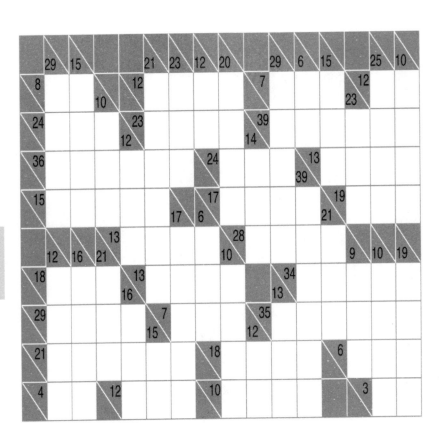

PUZZLE 96

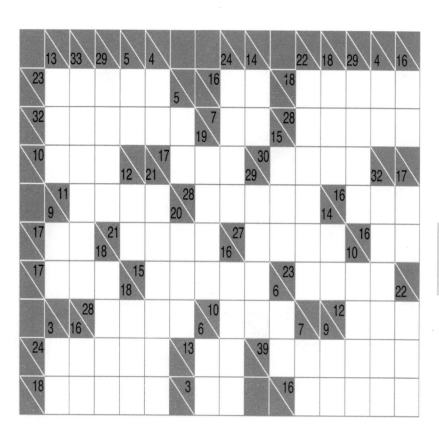

FIENDISH

PUZZLE 97

FIENDISH

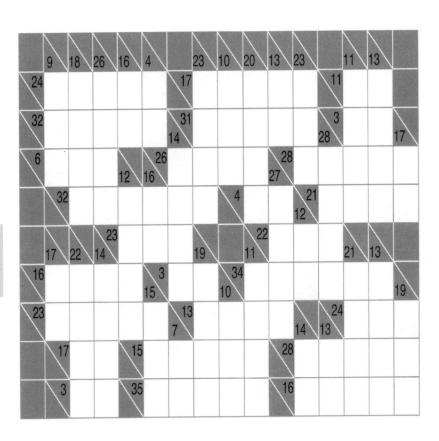

PUZZLE 98

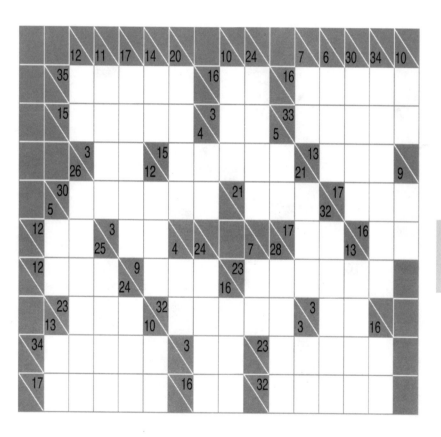

FIENDISH

PUZZLE 99

FIENDISH

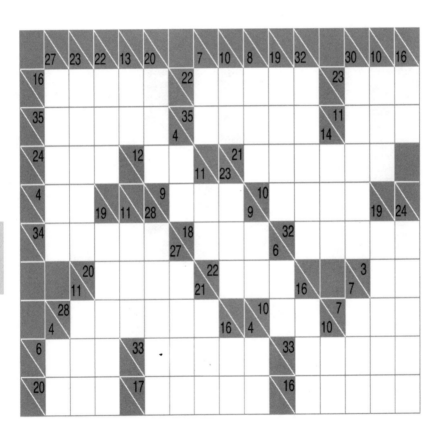

PUZZLE 100

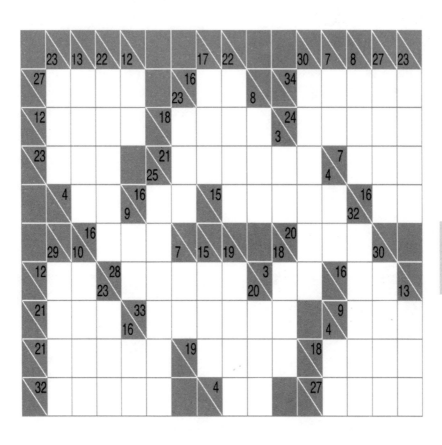

FIENDISH

Puzzle 1

Puzzle 2

Puzzle 3

Puzzle 4

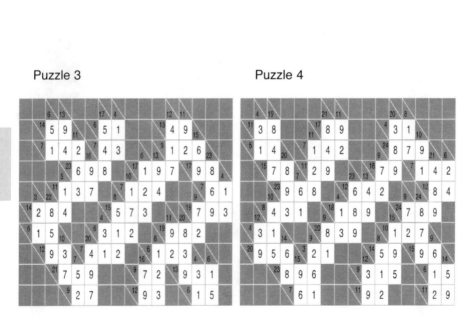

Puzzle 5

Puzzle 6

Puzzle 7

Puzzle 8

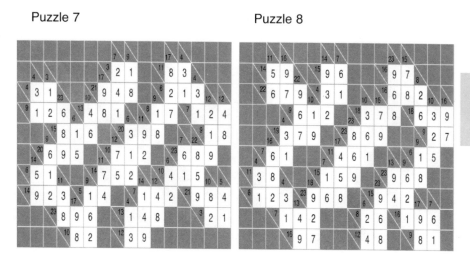

Puzzle 9

Puzzle 10

Puzzle 11

Puzzle 12

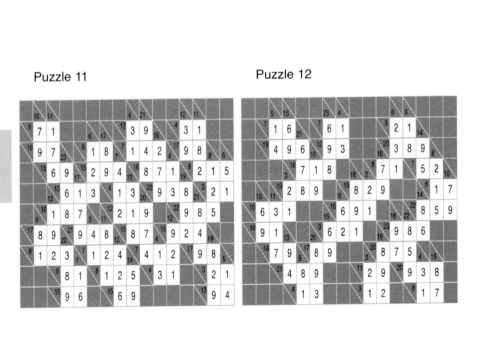

Puzzle 13

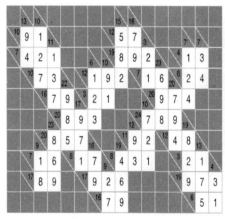

Puzzle 14

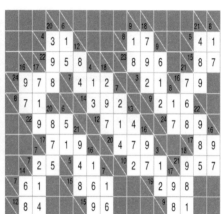

Puzzle 15

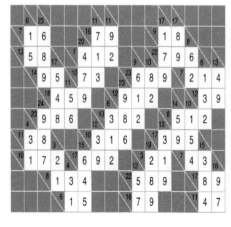

Puzzle 16

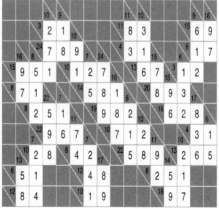

Puzzle 17

Puzzle 18

Puzzle 19

Puzzle 20

Puzzle 21

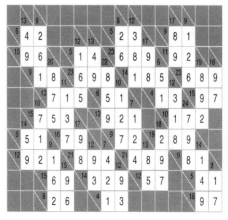

Puzzle 22

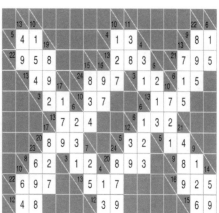

Puzzle 23

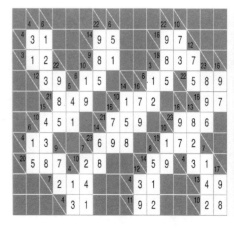

Puzzle 24

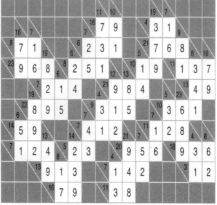

Puzzle 25

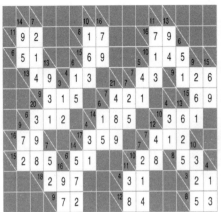

Puzzle 26

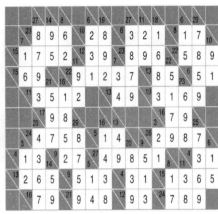

Puzzle 27

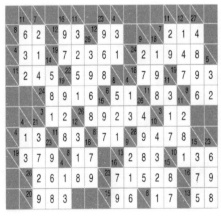

Puzzle 28

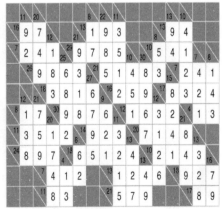

Puzzle 29

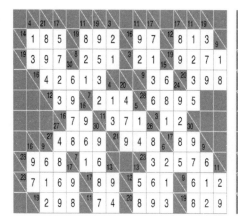

Puzzle 30

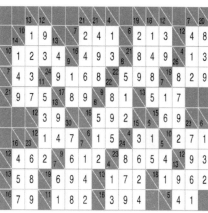

Puzzle 31

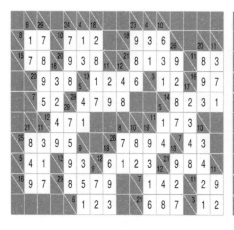

Puzzle 32

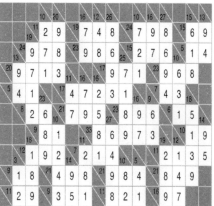

Puzzle 33

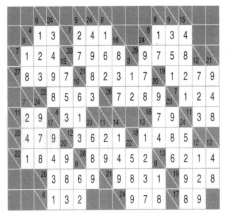

Puzzle 34

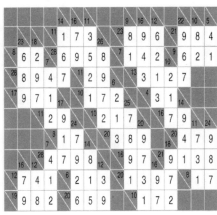

Puzzle 35

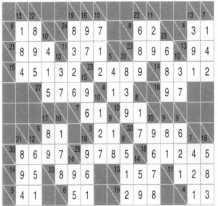

Puzzle 36

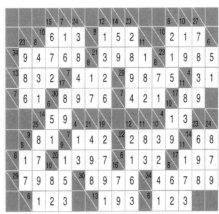

Puzzle 37

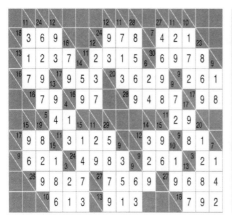

Puzzle 38

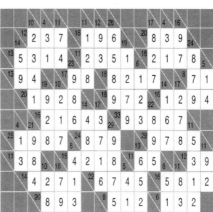

Puzzle 39

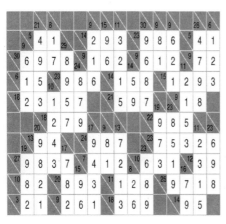

Puzzle 40

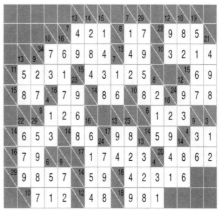

Puzzle 41

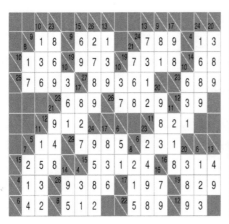

Puzzle 42

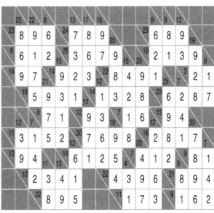

Puzzle 43

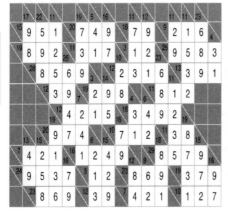

Puzzle 44

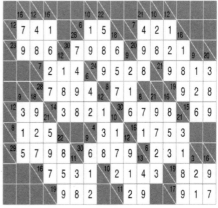

Puzzle 45

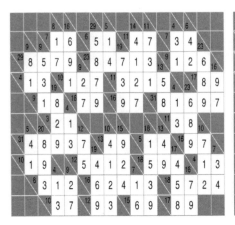

Puzzle 46

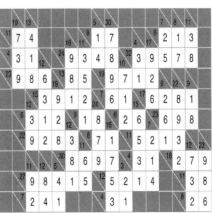

Puzzle 47

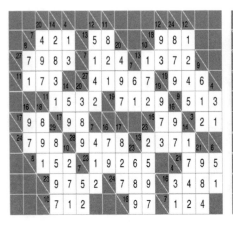

Puzzle 48

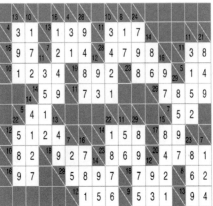

Puzzle 49

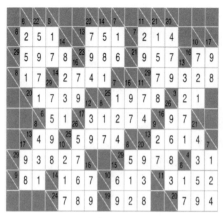

Puzzle 50

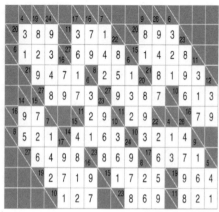

Puzzle 51

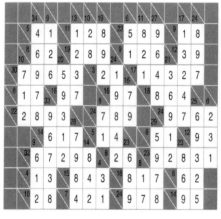

Puzzle 52

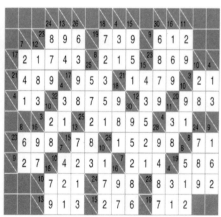

Puzzle 53

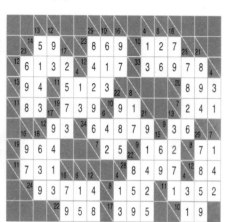

Puzzle 54

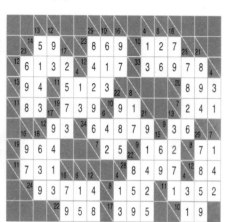

Puzzle 55

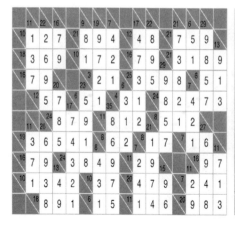

Puzzle 56

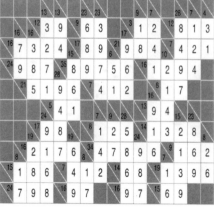

Puzzle 57

Puzzle 58

Puzzle 59

Puzzle 60

Puzzle 61

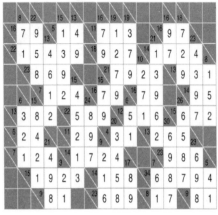

Puzzle 62

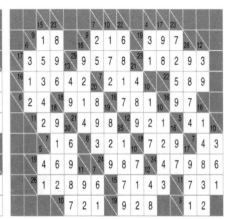

Puzzle 63

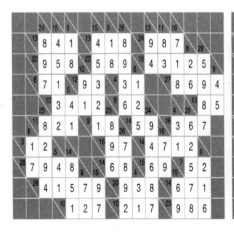

Puzzle 64

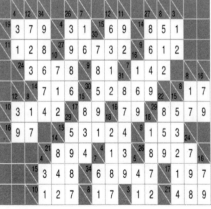

SOLUTIONS

Puzzle 65

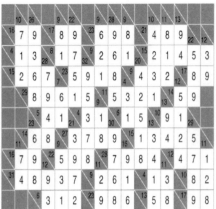

Puzzle 66

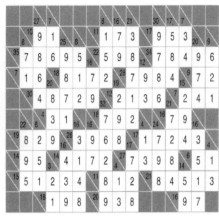

Puzzle 67

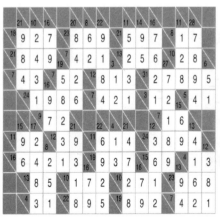

Puzzle 68

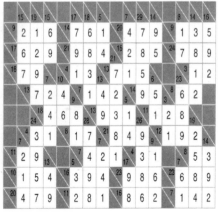

SOLUTIONS

Puzzle 69

Puzzle 70

Puzzle 71

Puzzle 72

Puzzle 73

Puzzle 74

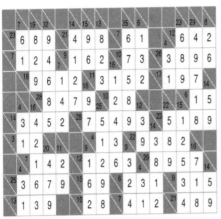

Puzzle 75

Puzzle 76

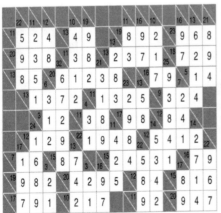

Puzzle 77

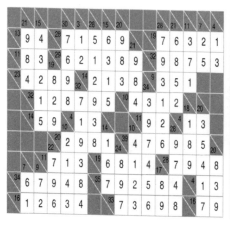

Puzzle 78

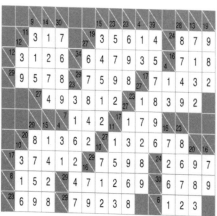

Puzzle 79

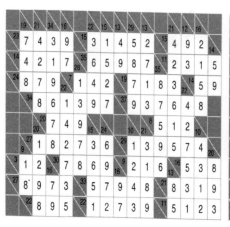

Puzzle 80

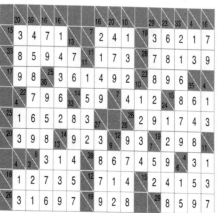

Puzzle 81

Puzzle 82

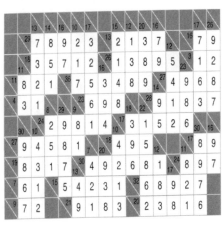

Puzzle 83

Puzzle 84

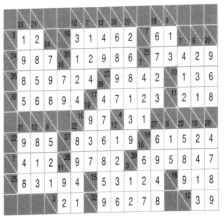